THE BOOK THIEF

by
Markus Zusak

Student Packet

Written by
Jackie Crnkovich

Contains masters for:

3	Prereading Activities
7	Vocabulary Activities
1	Study Guide
3	Literary Analysis Activities
3	Character Analysis Activities
3	Critical Thinking Activities
1	Comprehension Activity
1	Writing Activity
6	Quizzes
1	Novel Test

PLUS Detailed Answer Key
and Scoring Rubric

Teacher Note

Selected activities, quizzes, and test questions in this Novel Units® Student Packet are labeled with the appropriate reading/language arts skills for quick reference. These skills can be found above quiz/test questions or sections and in the activity headings.

Note

The 2007 Knopf trade paperback edition of the novel, © 2005 by Markus Zusak, was used to prepare this guide. Page references may differ in other editions. Novel ISBN: 978-0-375-84220-7

Please note: Parts of this novel deal with sensitive, mature issues. Please assess the appropriateness of this book for the age level and maturity of your students prior to reading and discussing it with them.

ISBN 978-1-56137-577-6

To order, contact your local school supply store, or—
Novel Units, Inc.
P.O. Box 97
Bulverde, TX 78163-0097

Web site: novelunits.com

Note to the Teacher

Selected activities, quizzes, and test questions in this Novel Units® Student Packet are labeled with the following reading/language arts skills for quick reference. These skills can be found above quiz/test questions or sections and in the activity headings.

Basic Understanding: The student will demonstrate a basic understanding of written texts. The student will:
- use a text's structure or other sources to locate and recall information (Locate Information)
- determine main idea and identify relevant facts and details (Main Idea and Details)
- use prior knowledge and experience to comprehend and bring meaning to a text (Prior Knowledge)
- summarize major ideas in a text (Summarize Major Ideas)

Literary Elements: The student will apply knowledge of literary elements to understand written texts. The student will:
- analyze characters from a story (Character Analysis)
- analyze conflict and problem resolution (Conflict/Resolution)
- recognize and interpret literary devices (flashback, foreshadowing, symbolism, simile, metaphor, etc.) (Literary Devices)
- consider characters' points of view (Point of View)
- recognize and analyze a story's setting (Setting)
- understand and explain themes in a text (Theme)

Analyze Written Texts: The student will use a variety of strategies to analyze written texts. The student will:
- identify the author's purpose (Author's Purpose)
- identify cause and effect relationships in a text (Cause/Effect)
- identify characteristics representative of a given genre (Genre)
- interpret information given in a text (Interpret Text)
- make and verify predictions with information from a text (Predictions)
- sequence events in chronological order (Sequencing)
- identify and use multiple text formats (Text Format)
- follow written directions and write directions for others to follow (Follow/Write Directions)

Critical Thinking: The student will apply critical-thinking skills to analyze written texts. The student will:
- write and complete analogies (Analogies)
- find similarities and differences throughout a text (Compare/Contrast)
- draw conclusions from information given (Drawing Conclusions)
- make and explain inferences (Inferences)
- respond to texts by making connections and observations (Making Connections)
- recognize and identify the mood of a text (Mood)
- recognize an author's style and how it affects a text (Style)
- support responses by referring to relevant aspects of a text (Support Responses)
- recognize and identify the author's tone (Tone)
- write to entertain, such as through humorous poetry or short stories (Write to Entertain)
- write to express ideas (Write to Express)
- write to inform (Write to Inform)
- write to persuade (Write to Persuade)
- demonstrate understanding by creating visual images based on text descriptions (Visualizing)
- practice math skills as they relate to a text (Math Skills)

Clue Search

Directions: Collect information about the novel for each of the items. Write down the information, and then make some predictions about the novel.

Information Source	Information Provided
Dedication	
Title	
Cover Illustration	
Teasers on the cover	
Friends' recommendations	
Reviewers' recommendations/awards won	

Your predictions about the novel:

Name _____

Anticipation Guide

Directions: Rate each of the following statements before you read the novel, and discuss your ratings with a partner. After you have completed the novel, rate and discuss the statements again.

1 ———— 2 ———— 3 ———— 4 ———— 5 ———— 6
strongly agree   strongly disagree

	Before	**After**
1. The power of words can be used for positive and negative purposes.	_____	_____
2. It is important to establish your own beliefs about political issues.	_____	_____
3. People of different nationalities can never be friendly toward one another.	_____	_____
4. Books can connect people who might otherwise have nothing in common.	_____	_____
5. It is justifiable to steal from someone if you are in need.	_____	_____
6. Blind obedience is often dangerous.	_____	_____
7. People that oppose their national leader should be punished.	_____	_____
8. Kindness should always be offered, even to those we do not know.	_____	_____
9. It is impossible to cheat death.	_____	_____
10. Sometimes loving someone means leaving them.	_____	_____

Name _____

The Importance of Books In My Life

Directions: Write a three- to four-paragraph essay responding to the following: What
has your attitude about books and reading been throughout your life? Is reading books
important to you, or is it something you regard as a chore? How would your life be affected
if you did not have access to books?

_____

_____

_____

_____

_____

_____

_____

_____

_____

_____

_____

_____

_____

_____

_____

_____

_____

_____

Name _____

Vocabulary Card Game

affable	septic	innocuously	echelons
prolific	castigate	stupefyingly	incense
auspicious	raucous	lechery	misogynistic
audacious	nefarious		

Teacher Directions:

- Photocopy and cut out the following pages.

- Give one card to each student in the class.

- The student who has the starred card begins by reading his/her question.

- The student who has the card with the correct vocabulary word responds and then reads his/her question.

- Play continues in this manner until all cards have been read.

☆ **affable**

Who has a word that means
infected or putrid?

---

septic

Who has a word that means
in a way not likely to
irritate or offend?

---

innocuously

Who has a word that means
levels of command, authority, or rank?

---

echelons

Who has a word that means
producing in high quantity
or with great frequency?

---

prolific

Who has a word that means
to criticize or reprimand severely?

---

castigate

Who has a word that means
so surprisingly impressive as to stun
or overwhelm?

stupefyingly -- Who has a word that means to make angry or enrage?	**incense** -- Who has a word that means promising success?
auspicious -- Who has a word that means harsh, strident, or rowdy?	**raucous** -- Who has a word that means free indulgence of lust or lewdness?
lechery -- Who has a word that means of or characterized by a hatred of women?	**misogynistic** -- Who has a word that means fearlessly and often recklessly daring?
audacious -- Who has a word that means wicked in the extreme?	**nefarious** -- Who has a word that means friendly or warmly polite?

Vocabulary Sentence Sets

disheveled	luminary	morbidity	perusing
melancholic	lamented	flippant	crux
culminate	fruition	partisans	infernal
kinetic	consummate	culpability	jocular
melee	brandished	euphoric	pensive

Directions: Choose 15 vocabulary words from the list above. Write the words on the numbered lines below.

1. _____ 2. _____

3. _____ 4. _____

5. _____ 6. _____

7. _____ 8. _____

9. _____ 10. _____

11. _____ 12. _____

13. _____ 14. _____

15. _____

On a separate sheet of paper, use each of the following sets of words in an original sentence. Your sentences should show that you know the meanings of the vocabulary words as they are used in the story.

Sentence 1: words 8 and 4
Sentence 2: words 9 and 3
Sentence 3: words 1 and 10
Sentence 4: words 11 and 7
Sentence 5: words 15 and 13
Sentence 6: words 3 and 6
Sentence 7: words 12 and 4
Sentence 8: words 14 and 9
Sentence 9: words 5 and 2
Sentence 10: words 7 and 6

Name _____

Word Map

prattled	havoc	conglomerate	incongruous
proffer	malignant	apex	morose
ostracism	capitulate	archetypal	emulate
tirade	dormant	inaugural	

Directions: Choose seven of the vocabulary words above, and complete a word map for each.

Synonyms	Magazine cut-out, drawing, or symbol that shows what the word means
_____	
_____	
_____	
_____	
_____	
_____	

Word

_____

Definition in your own words	Word used in a sentence
_____	_____
_____	_____
_____	_____

Vocabulary Chart

imperative	beleaguered	sadistic	sporadic
hiatus	self-deprecation	caustic	malice
envisaged	vociferously	debilitate	pallid
litany	sodden	rhetoric	charisma
deviants	microcosm	diminutive	epitome
altercation			

Directions: Write each vocabulary word in the left-hand column of the chart. Complete the chart by placing a check mark in the column that best describes your familiarity with each word. Working with a partner, find and read the line where each word appears in the story. Find the meaning of each word in the dictionary. Together with your partner, choose ten of the words checked in the last column. On a separate sheet of paper, use each of those words in a sentence.

Vocabulary Word	I Can Define	I Have Seen/Heard	New Word For Me

© Novel Units, Inc.

Vocabulary by Association

unflappable	paradox	incredulous	serpentined
copiously	trepidation	nonplussed	formidable
animosity	bulbous	stoic	opus
nonchalance	hapless	temerity	
vindication			

Directions: Define and associate each vocabulary word above with a character from the novel. In the chart below, explain why that word matches your chosen character's personality. You may associate more than one word with a character, but use no more than three words per character.

Word(s)	Character	Explanation

Name _____

Vocabulary Synonyms

cannier	conglomeration	doggedly	miscreants
livid	admonished	vigil	

Directions: Circle the correct synonym for each vocabulary word, and then use each vocabulary word in a sentence.

1.	**cannier**	shrewder	harder	quicker
2.	**conglomeration**	mess	promise	cluster
3.	**doggedly**	friendly	tenaciously	rapidly
4.	**miscreants**	daredevils	liars	villains
5.	**livid**	furious	ugly	energetic
6.	**admonished**	carried	applauded	reproved
7.	**vigil**	folk tale	watch	companion

1. _____

   _____

2. _____

   _____

3. _____

   _____

4. _____

   _____

5. _____

   _____

6. _____

   _____

7. _____

   _____

Crossword Puzzle

propaganda	indignant	metronome	buoyed
semblance	quell	implored	obliterated
bereaved	resolute	desecrated	insufferable
lustrous	detriment	apocalyptic	lolling

Directions: Select ten vocabulary words from above. Create a crossword puzzle answer key by filling in the grid below. Be sure to number the squares for each word. Blacken any spaces not used by the letters. Then, write clues to the crossword puzzle. Number the clues to match the numbers in the squares. The teacher will give each student a blank grid. Make a blank copy of your crossword puzzle for other students to answer. Exchange your clues with someone else, and solve the blank puzzle s/he gives you. Check the completed puzzles with the answer keys.

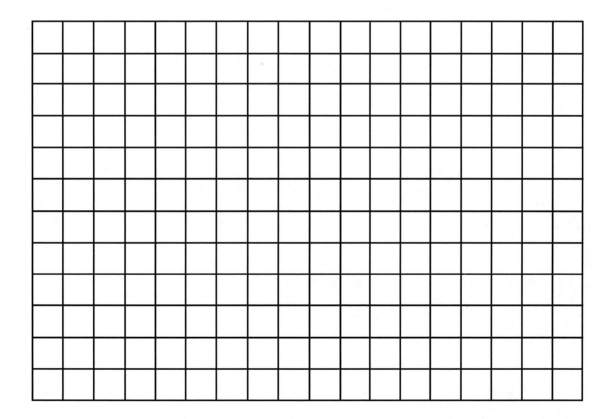

Name _____

Directions: Answer the following questions on a separate sheet of paper. Use your answers in class discussions, for writing assignments, and to review for tests.

Death and Chocolate–The Kiss (A Childhood Decision Maker)

1. What does Death identify as his "saving grace"?
2. What appears to be the situation described in the chapter "Beside the Railway Line"?
3. Describe the setting the second time Death sees the book thief.
4. Why does Death describe the third time he sees the book thief as red?
5. What does Liesel pick up from her brother's gravesite?
6. What does the book thief mean when she writes, "…the journey continued like *everything* had happened" (p. 25)?
7. How does Liesel respond when she is brought to her foster family, the Hubermanns?
8. What makes Liesel's eyes "dangerous"?
9. What word does Liesel associate with the memory of her father?
10. What does Rosa tell Liesel to call her and Hans?
11. What does Hans do in the mornings to comfort and entertain Liesel?
12. Why is school in Molching painful for Liesel?
13. What organization does Liesel join when she turns ten?
14. Where does Hans go many nights to make money?
15. For which of her washing customers does Rosa have the greatest disdain? Why?
16. What does Frau Holtzapfel do every time she passes by the Hubermanns' door?
17. What must any customer of Frau Diller do to get served?
18. What are the terms of Rudy and Liesel's race?

The Jesse Owens Incident–Dead Letters

1. What astonishing thing does Rudy do at the Hubert Oval?
2. Who is Mr. Kaufmann?
3. What does Hans discover under the mattress when Liesel wets her bed?
4. What does Hans begin doing the night Liesel wets the bed?
5. When they run out of sandpaper, how do Liesel and Hans write their words and pictures?
6. What does Liesel consider to be the "smell of friendship"?

Name _____

7. Why is Liesel moved out of the younger class and put in the class with children her own age?

8. What happens when Liesel stands before the class to read?

9. What does Liesel do to Schmeikl when he teases her about her reading ability?

10. To what does Death attribute the success of the Nazi Party in Germany?

11. How did the Hubermanns pay for the books they bought Liesel for Christmas?

12. What bad news does Rosa's customer Ernst Vogel give her?

13. Why does Rosa decide to send out Liesel to deal with her customers?

14. To whom does Liesel write for her school letter-writing assignment?

Hitler's Birthday, 1940–The Attributes of Summer

1. For what big event is Molching preparing?

2. From Death's description, what can the reader infer has happened on "the road of yellow stars" (p. 102)?

3. What is the main source of tension between Hans Jr. and his father?

4. What hurtful thing does Hans Jr. call his father?

5. What does the Nazi speaking at the bonfire say that greatly disturbs Liesel?

6. Whom does Liesel help at the bonfire?

7. What does Hans do when Liesel says she hates Hitler?

8. What happens when Liesel puts the book under her shirt?

9. What does Hans buy at the Nazi Party office?

10. Why is Liesel afraid to pick up wash from the mayor's wife?

11. What wondrous thing does the mayor's wife show Liesel?

12. What items does the man bring to the Jew hidden in the basement?

13. Why is *The Shoulder Shrug* a banned book?

14. What does the reader learn about the mayor's wife that explains her odd behavior?

15. What do Liesel and Rudy do to combat their hunger?

The Aryan Shopkeeper–Liesel's Lecture

1. What do Liesel and Rudy buy and share at Frau Diller's?

2. What is ironic about the way Max avoids detection on the train?

3. Who helps Max escape the Nazis?

4. What is the English translation of *Mein Kampf*? Why is its meaning ironic to Max?

5. What plan do Rudy and Liesel devise to rob Otto Sturm?

6. What does Arthur Berg want Rudy and Liesel to do with Otto's food basket?

7. What happens when the gang steals from the potato farmer?

8. What does Max do to propel himself forward on his walk to the Hubermanns' home?

9. What does Max ask Hans upon entering his house?

10. What assignment was Hans Hubermann given the morning the rest of his company went into battle?

11. What promise did Hans make to Erik Vandenburg's widow?

12. Why did Hans start losing painting customers?

13. What does Hans do for Joel Kleinmann, his "second" mistake?

14. What happened on June 16, 1939? Why do you think it is so firmly etched in Hans' mind?

15. How did Max and Walter Kugler's friendship develop?

16. What does Max's mother hand him before he escapes with Walter?

17. What had Hans done with the copy of *Mein Kampf* he purchased on the night of Hitler's birthday?

18. How does Rosa respond to Max's arrival?

19. What threats does Hans make to instill in Liesel the importance of keeping Max secret?

The Sleeper–The Gamblers (A Seven-Sided Die)

1. What similarities between herself and Max does Liesel recognize right away?

2. What does Max believe are the two most pitiful words he can say? Why does he feel this way?

3. What price does Max pay for wanting to live?

4. What changes does Liesel notice in Rosa after the arrival of Max?

5. What does the family tell Trudy about Max when she comes to visit at Christmas? Why?

6. To what does Liesel liken Max's freshly-washed hair?

7. How does Max respond to Liesel's question about whether *Mein Kampf* is a good book?

8. What do Max and Liesel share that brings a "small breakthrough" in their relationship?

9. What does Liesel give Max on her birthday? How does this affect him?

10. On what does Max compose his story, *The Standover Man*?

11. What is meant by the words, "She saw an imaginary framed photo seep into the wall—a quiet-smiled secret" (p. 238)?

12. What reason does Death give for revealing the ending of the story?

13. What does Liesel imagine herself telling the mayor's wife one day as she reads in the library?

14. What is Max's favorite part of the newspapers Liesel brings home?

15. What does Max paint on the basement wall?

16. What does Max daydream about to pass the time in the basement?

17. Why does the mayor fire Rosa?

18. Whom does Liesel see while she is yelling at the mayor's wife? Why do you think she sees this person?

Rudy's Youth–The Floating Book (Part II)

1. What does Rudy do to earn his extra laps and drills from Franz Deutscher?

2. What sets Viktor Chemmel apart from the other members of the fruit-stealing gang?

3. What is the subject of the book Max writes?

4. What humiliating event makes Rudy hungry for a victory?

5. What does Liesel steal from the mayor's house?

6. What do Liesel and Rudy leave behind at the mayor's house?

7. What does Rudy get caught stealing from the grocer?

8. What question does Rudy purposely answer incorrectly?

9. What final humiliation does Franz put Rudy through?

10. How is Rudy's refusal to attend Hitler Youth finally resolved?

11. What does Viktor Chemmel do to get his revenge on Rudy?

Death's Diary: 1942–Death's Diary: The Parisians

1. Whom does Death say he looks like?

2. What do Liesel, Max, and the Hubermanns make in the basement at Christmas?

3. What does Death say happened when he came for Max on Himmel Street that winter?

4. What is the first "gift" Liesel brings to Max while he is sick?

5. How does Liesel give Max a cloud?

6. What makes Liesel choose *The Dream Carrier* in her second theft from the mayor's library?

7. What does Death suggest about the mayor's open windows?

8. What potential problem does Liesel overhear Rosa and Hans discussing?

9. Describe the disturbing dream Liesel has.

10. On what pretext does Rosa come to the school to tell Liesel Max has awakened?

11. What does Rosa hand Liesel before she leaves the school?

12. What does Death describe falling from the sky after the bombing of Cologne?

13. Why is the NSDAP inspecting basements?

14. How does Liesel get word to Hans about the basement inspections?

15. How does Death feel about having to collect all of the dead during the war?

Champagne and Accordions–The Idiot and the Coat Men

1. Why does Hans' painting business pick up in the summer of 1942?

2. What indispensable item do Liesel and Hans bring on all his painting jobs?

3. With what does one of Hans' more wealthy clients pay him for a painting job?

4. What prevents Liesel from asking Hans to teach her to play the accordion?

5. Why does Rudy fail to win the fourth race? Do you believe that he did this on purpose? Why or why not?

6. Why does Liesel choose *A Song in the Dark* as her next stolen book?

7. What is tucked inside the dictionary Liesel steals from the mayor's house?

8. What does Max confess to having done during the first bomb scare?

9. What does Liesel do in the bomb shelter that calms people's fears?

10. What damage does Molching suffer in the first bombing?

11. What does Frau Holtzapfel want Liesel to do for her in exchange for coffee rations?

12. What does Hans do during the march of the Jewish prisoners?

13. What is the major repercussion of Hans' gesture?

14. What does Max write in the note he leaves for Hans?

15. Why does Hans wish the Nazis would come for him?

Dominoes and Darkness–The Anarchist's Suit Collection

1. What game are Rudy and his sisters playing while the black-coated men talk to his parents?

2. What do the men want with Rudy? Why do the Steiners resist?

3. How are Hans and Alex Steiner punished for their respective crimes against the Nazi Party?

4. How does Rosa wake Hans the morning he leaves for the army?

5. Where does Rudy claim to be walking when he and Liesel head out of town one day?

6. What poignant thing does Liesel find Rosa doing one night?

7. What jobs are Alex Steiner and Hans given in the army?

8. Why does Hans' crew misdirect the woman looking for her son from what was most certainly his body?

9. What turns out to be one of Liesel's favorite distractions from worrying about Max, Hans, and Alex Steiner?

10. What do Rudy and Liesel put on the road before the Jews are paraded by?

11. What does Rosa pull out from under the mattress for Liesel?

12. According to *The Word Shaker*, how did Hitler get the idea to rule the world with words?

13. What does Liesel give Rudy for Christmas?

The Next Temptation–Homecoming

1. What had Ilsa Hermann left on the windowsill for Liesel?

2. What is embroidered on Ilsa Hermann's bathrobe and slippers?

3. Why does Reinhold Zucker grow to despise Hans?

4. What happened to Michael Holtzapfel's hand?

5. How did Robert Holtzapfel die?

6. What does Liesel return to the Hermanns' house?

7. How does Rosa spend her nights while Hans is gone?

8. What is ironic about the way Reinhold Zucker dies?

9. Why does Hans get sent home?

10. What reason does Rudy give for bringing a teddy bear along on his thefts?

11. What happens to Rudy's "career" as a thief?

12. What does Frau Holtzapfel do when the air raids begin again?

13. With whom does Liesel come face to face in the airplane?

14. What does Rudy give the pilot of the downed plane to comfort him at the moment of his death?

15. Who arrives at the Hubermanns' at the end of this section?

The End of the World (Part I)–The Handover Man

1. Why is Liesel the only person to survive the final bombing on Himmel Street?

2. How does Death describe the souls of Rosa and Hans Hubermann?

3. Why does Michael Holtzapfel kill himself?

4. What does Death imagine is happening in Frau Holtzapfel's kitchen as she faces her grief?

5. What does Liesel quote the second time she jumps into the line of marching Jews?

6. What happens to Max and Liesel when they are discovered by the Nazi guard?

7. What does Liesel realize as she is confiding to Rudy about Max?

8. Why does Liesel tear up the book in Ilsa Hermann's library?

9. Why does Ilsa Hermann come to Liesel's house?

10. What does Liesel do when she finds Rudy's body?

11. What vision does Liesel have as she says goodbye to Hans?

12. What does Death take from the back of the garbage truck?

13. Where does Liesel die?

14. Where does Liesel go after the Hubermanns die?

15. Who walks into Alex Steiner's shop after the war?

16. What does Death give Liesel when he comes to take her soul away?

17. What is Death's final revelation to Liesel and the reader? Why do you suppose he feels this way?

Name _____

Story Map

Directions: Fill in each box below with information about the novel.

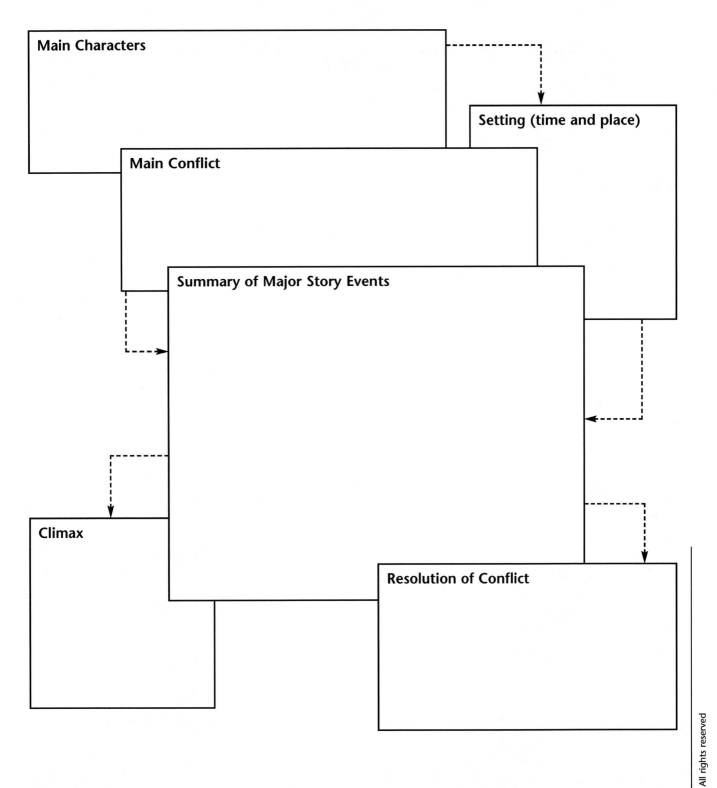

Main Characters

Setting (time and place)

Main Conflict

Summary of Major Story Events

Climax

Resolution of Conflict

Sorting Characters

Directions: Similarities between characters are sometimes a clue to themes in a story. Place this novel's characters in one or more of the groups below.

Victims	Victimizers	Fighters
Peace-lovers	**Conformists**	**Self-directors**

Understanding Values

Values represent people's beliefs about what is important, good, or worthwhile. For example, most families value spending time together.

Directions: Think about the following characters from the novel and the values they exhibit. What do they value? What beliefs do they have about what is important, good, or worthwhile? On the chart below, list each character's three most important values, from most important to least. Be prepared to share your lists during a class discussion.

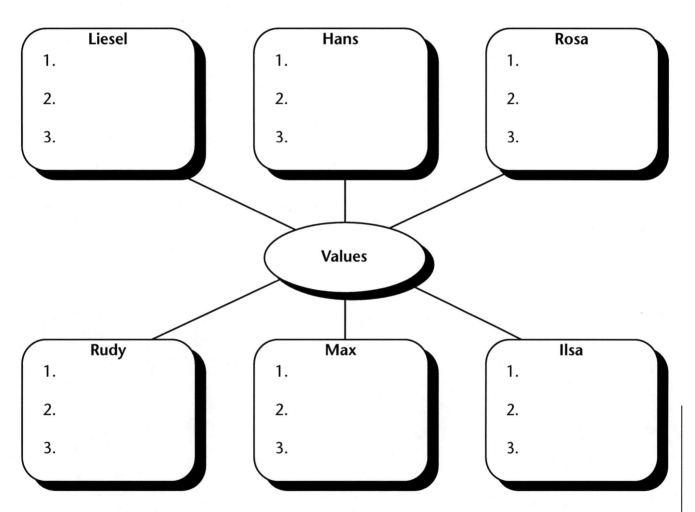

After you have finished the chart and participated in the class discussion, think about which character seems to have values most like your own. Write a paragraph that explains why you chose this character.

Name _____

Character Growth

Directions: Characters often "grow" throughout a novel as they learn and change. Choose a character from the novel who shows evidence of growth. Write the character's name in the center of the tree rings below. In the surrounding rings, write either examples of the character's growth or events that cause the growth. Write the examples or events in the order they occurred in the novel.

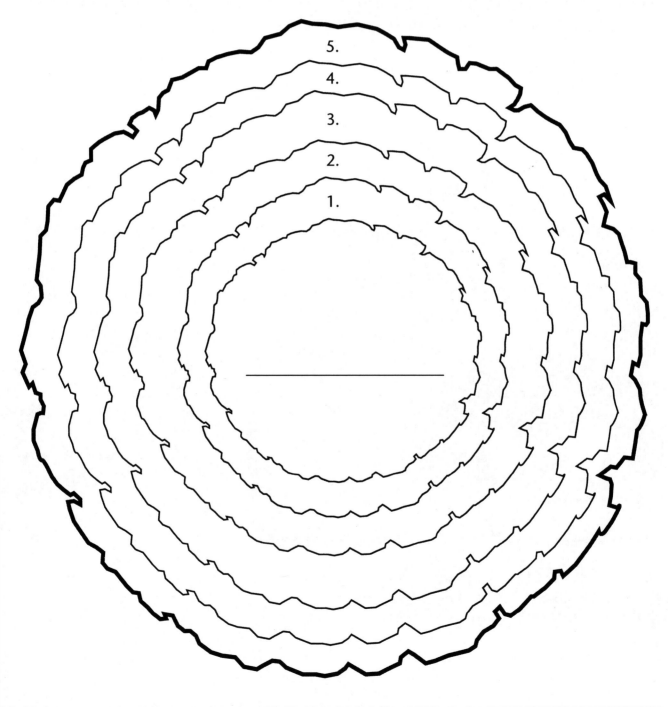

Name _____

Sociogram

Directions: On the "spokes" surrounding each character's name, write several adjectives that describe that character. How does one character influence another? On the arrows joining one character to another, write a description of the relationship between the two characters.

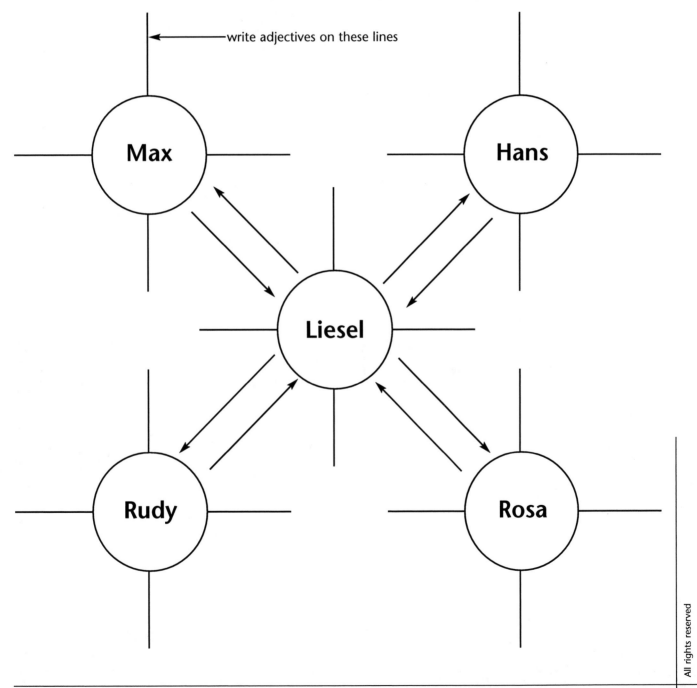

Effects of Reading

Directions: When reading, each part of a novel may affect you in a different way. Think about how parts of the novel affected you in different ways. Did some parts make you laugh? cry? want to do something to help someone? Below, list one part of the novel that touched each of the following parts of the body: your head (made you think), your heart (made you feel), your funny bone (made you laugh), or your feet (spurred you to action).

Your head	Your heart

Your funny bone	Your feet

Sequencing Events

Directions: In the boxes below, illustrate the series of events that led to the ultimate fate of one of the following characters: Max, Liesel, Rudy.

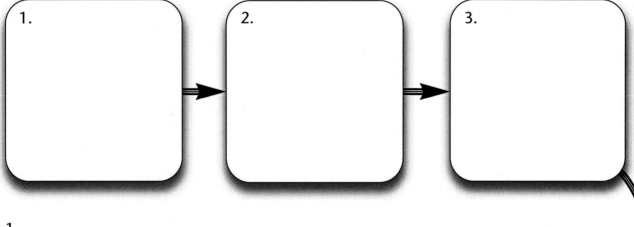

1. _____

2. _____

3. _____

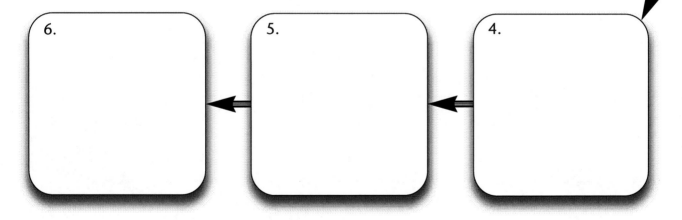

4. _____

5. _____

6. _____

Conflict

The **conflict** of a story is the struggle between two people or two forces. There are four main types of conflict: person vs. person, person vs. nature, person vs. society, and person vs. self.

Directions: In the space provided, list four conflicts a character experiences and justify why you identify it with that particular type of conflict. Then explain how each conflict is resolved in the story.

person vs. person

Conflict	Resolution

person vs. nature

Conflict	Resolution

person vs. society

Conflict	Resolution

person vs. self

Conflict	Resolution

Name _____

Thematic Analysis

Directions: Choose a theme from the novel to be the focus of your word web. Complete the web, and then answer the question in each starred box.

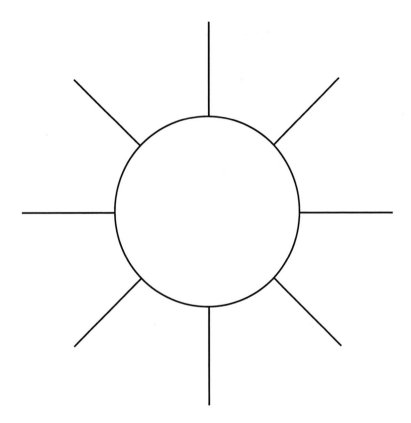

 What is the author's
main message?

 What did you learn
from the novel?

Name _____

Attribute Web

Directions: In the boxes surrounding the oval, list ways in which the power of words affected a particular character from the novel. Be sure to write the name of the character in the box.

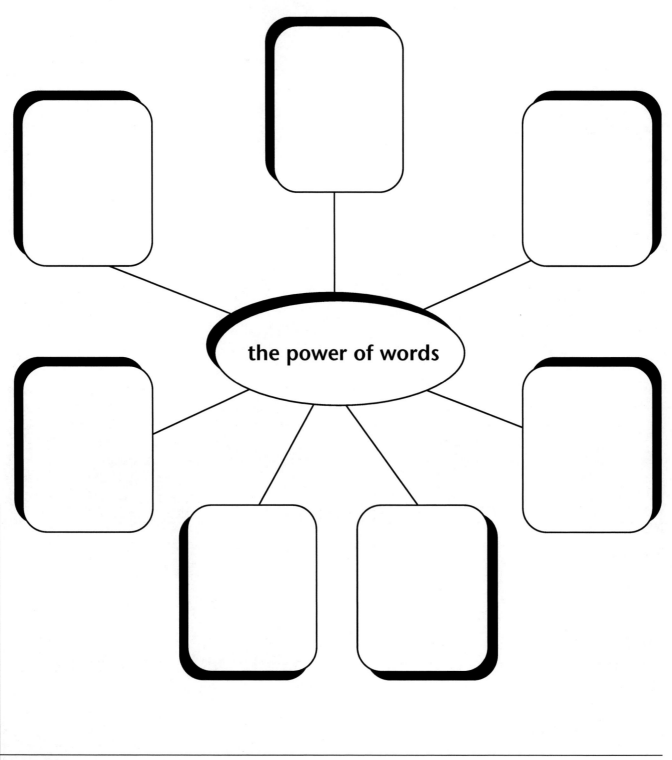

Max and Liesel's Reunion

Directions: The author does not provide specific details of Max and Liesel's reunion at Alex Steiner's shop. On the lines below, continue the chapter titled "Max" and explain what happened when Max found Liesel after World War II.

_____

_____

_____

_____

_____

_____

_____

_____

_____

_____

_____

_____

_____

_____

_____

_____

_____

_____

_____

_____

Name _____

(Character Analysis)
A. Identification: Match each character with the correct description.

_____ 1. Nazi shop owner who demands a "*Heil* Hitler" from every customer

_____ 2. dies on the train and haunts Liesel

_____ 3. the book thief

_____ 4. mischievous boy who pretends he is Jesse Owens

_____ 5. man known for his foul language and whistling

_____ 6. kind and gentle man who plays the accordion

_____ 7. tailor who goes along with the Nazis to protect his family

_____ 8. boy Liesel beats in the schoolyard for teasing her

_____ 9. the novel's narrator

_____ 10. woman with a harsh tongue; hits people with her wooden spoon

_____ 11. boy whose partial deafness often gets him in trouble

a. Liesel Meminger

b. Pfiffikus

c. Alex Steiner

d. Rosa Hubermann

e. Hans Hubermann

f. Frau Diller

g. Ludwig Schmeikl

h. Werner Meminger

i. Tommy Müller

j. Rudy Steiner

k. Death

(Summarize Major Ideas)
B. Short Answer: Write a brief answer for each of the following.

12. In what time and place is the story set?

_____

13. Why does Liesel come to live with the Hubermanns?

_____

14. What is the subject matter of the first book the book thief steals?

_____

15. What do the Hubermanns do for a living?

_____

16. Why does Liesel get in a fight in the schoolyard?

_____

© Novel Units, Inc.

Name _____

(Main Idea and Details)
A. Fill in the Blanks

1. Max's favorite pasttime as a youth was _____.

2. In World War I, Erik Vandenburg taught Hans to _____.

3. Otto Sturm is taking food to _____ when Liesel and Rudy assault him.

4. Hans does not go into battle with the rest of his troop because he is selected to _____.

5. One thing Hans sends Walter to help with Max's escape is a _____.

6. The title *Mein Kampf* means _____ in English.

7. When Mr. Kleinmann's shop is vandalized by Nazis, Hans helps him by _____.

(Main Idea and Details)
B. True/False: Mark each with a *T* for true or an *F* for false.

____ 8. When Liesel and Rudy find a *pfenning* in the street, they buy a piece of candy from Frau Diller.

____ 9. When Liesel and Rudy steal from Otto Sturm, they keep all the food for themselves.

____ 10. Max vehemently refuses to leave his family the night Walter comes to hide him.

____ 11. One of the questions Max asks Hans when he arrives is, "Do you still play the accordion?" (p. 173).

____ 12. Walter Kugler beat Max in the majority of their fights.

____ 13. Rosa argues with Hans about letting Max hide in their house.

____ 14. Hans threatens to burn Liesel's books if she tells anyone about Max.

(Literary Devices)
C. Literary Devices: Identify each of the following as simile, metaphor, personification, or metonymy.

_____15. "Fingermarks clutched the book" (p. 157).

_____16. "…he was…skinny as a whittled broom handle" (p. 187).

_____17. "…a voice stooped out and ambled toward the sergeant" (p. 177).

_____18. "the pop-up cheekbones; and the pothole eyes" (pp. 188–189)

Name _____

(Character Analysis)

A. Identification: Match each character with the correct description. You may use each character more than once.

____ 1. writer of *The Standover Man*

____ 2. sadistic Hitler Youth leader

____ 3. has hair like feathers

____ 4. jumps into the river to retrieve a book

____ 5. gives Max a haircut

____ 6. owns a beautiful library

____ 7. throws a rock at Franz

____ 8. lost a child in World War I

____ 9. is defended when he is unable to perform well in the Hitler Youth

____ 10. new leader of the fruit-stealing gang

____ 11. ends up face down in cow manure

____ 12. gets caught stealing a potato

____ 13. gives Rudy a haircut

____ 14. purposefully keeps the house very cold

____ 15. throws Liesel's book in the river

____ 16. "a good woman for a crisis"

____ 17. keeps a promise to his friend's widow

____ 18. will not give Hitler's real birthday

____ 19. dreams of boxing Adolf Hitler

____ 20. uses paint cans and drop cloths to hide Max

a. Liesel Meminger

b. Rosa Hubermann

c. Max Vandenburg

d. Ilsa Hermann

e. Tommy Müller

f. Franz Deutscher

g. Rudy Steiner

h. Viktor Chemmel

i. Hans Hubermann

(Support Responses)

B. Open-Ended Comprehension: On a separate sheet of paper, explain what, beyond hunger, drives Liesel and Rudy to steal something from the mayor's house.

Name _____

(Character Analysis)

A. Identification: Match each character with his/her quote.

_____ 1. "You told me to yell at you. You said they'd all believe it ….He woke up…. He's awake."

_____ 2. "To me, war is like the new boss who expects the impossible. He stands over your shoulder repeating one thing, incessantly: 'Get it done, get it done.'"

_____ 3. "I did it on purpose."

_____ 4. "I know you find me pathetic and loathsome,…but I must tell you that I am not so stupid as to not see your footprints in the library."

_____ 5. "There were stars….They burned my eyes."

_____ 6. "So I want you to come to my place and read it to me."

_____ 7. "I should have *known* not to give the man some bread. I just didn't think."

_____ 8. "Why did I have to bring all that snow down?… Why did I have to build that snowman?"

a. Frau Holtzapfel

b. Rosa Hubermann

c. Rudy Steiner

d. Hans Hubermann

e. Death

f. Liesel Meminger

g. Max Vandenburg

h. Ilsa Hermann

(Main Idea and Details)

B. True/False: Mark each with a *T* for true or an *F* for false.

_____ 9. Among the gifts Liesel brings Max is a deflated soccer ball.

_____ 10. Max tells Liesel his favorite gift was the leaf.

_____ 11. One of Hans' clients pays him with a bottle of whiskey.

_____ 12. The Nazi inspector is looking for basements that might make suitable bomb shelters.

_____ 13. Liesel reads from *Mein Kampf* to calm the neighbors' nerves in the bomb shelter.

_____ 14. Rudy wins all four running events in the Nazi Youth carnival.

_____ 15. Ilsa Hermann intentionally left the dictionary for Liesel to steal.

Name _____

(Summarize Major Ideas)
A. Short Answer: Write a brief answer for each of the following.

1. Why is Alex Steiner drafted into the army?

   _____

   _____

2. Who wrote *The Word Shaker*, and why?

   _____

   _____

3. What does Liesel find Rosa doing many nights while Hans is gone?

   _____

   _____

4. What does Rudy put on the road before the Jews parade by? What is the result?

   _____

   _____

5. What is Hans' job in the army?

   _____

   _____

6. Where does Liesel take Rudy on Christmas Eve? What gift does she give him?

   _____

   _____

7. What injury brings Hans home?

   _____

   _____

8. What news from the Russian front does Michael Holtzapfel bring his mother?

   _____

   _____

9. What does Rudy give the dying pilot?

   _____

   _____

10. Where had Rosa hidden *The Word Shaker*?

    _____

    _____

(Literary Elements)
A. Graphic Organizer: Complete the story map below.

Author	Setting	Main Characters

Title

Conflict	Themes	Author's Style/Tone

(Summarize Major Ideas)
B. Open-Ended Comprehension: Briefly describe the fates of at least five characters from the novel.

_____

_____

_____

_____

_____

_____

_____

Name _____

(Character Analysis)

A. Identification: Match each character with the correct description.

_____ 1. unfriendly neighbor given to spitting on the Hubermanns' door

_____ 2. goes from "fruit stealer to bread giver"

_____ 3. hangs himself for wanting to live

_____ 4. "a good woman for a crisis"

_____ 5. pulls a burning book from a fire

_____ 6. dies on the Russian front

_____ 7. Jewish fist fighter with hair like feathers

_____ 8. has "silver" eyes

_____ 9. taught Hans how to play the accordion

_____ 10. dies on a train as a young boy

_____ 11. man known for his vulgarity and whistling

_____ 12. throws Liesel's book in the river

_____ 13. cruel leader of Rudy's Hitler Youth division

_____ 14. drafted into the army for refusing to give his son over to the Nazi elite

_____ 15. demands the fateful seat in an army truck

_____ 16. keeps her house at an uncomfortable temperature to mourn her dead son

_____ 17. hides his childhood friend from the Nazis in Stuttgart

_____ 18. hearing loss has made him a bad marcher

_____ 19. store owner and staunch supporter of the Nazis

_____ 20. kind leader of the fruit-stealing gang

a. Michael Holtzapfel

b. Rudy Steiner

c. Alex Steiner

d. Rosa Hubermann

e. Viktor Chemmel

f. Hans Hubermann

g. Frau Diller

h. Liesel Meminger

i. Erik Vandenburg

j. Tommy Müller

k. Robert Holtzapfel

l. Frau Holtzapfel

m. Franz Deutscher

n. Reinhold Zucker

o. Walter Kugler

p. Pfiffikus

q. Werner Meminger

r. Max Vandenburg

s. Ilsa Hermann

t. Arthur Berg

(Literary Devices)
B. Literary Devices: Identify each of the following as simile, metaphor, personification, or metonymy.

_____21. "Behind him, a building groaned and tripped" (p. 433).

_____22. "Orange and red embers looked like rejected candy..." (p. 114).

_____23. "A balding brownshirt wasted no time in walking over and telling him to cut it out" (p. 363).

_____24. "...there were two monsters sitting in the kitchen" (p. 407).

(Character Analysis/Theme)
C. Identification: Identify the speaker of each quote below. Write a brief explanation of the passage's significance and how it highlights one of the novel's themes.

25. "As you can see, I have been in your library again and I have ruined one of your books. I was just so angry and afraid and I wanted to kill the words....To punish myself, I think I will stop coming here. Or is it punishment at all? I love this place and hate it, because it is full of words."

_____

_____

_____

26. "...I have the endless ability to be in the right place at the right time. The consequence of this is that I'm always finding humans at their best and worst. I see their ugly and their beauty, and I wonder how the same thing can be both."

_____

_____

_____

27. "There must be a place in heaven for those who have been where I have been. You might think I don't love you because of what I've done, but I do."

_____

_____

_____

28. "I am stupid....And kind. Which makes the biggest idiot in the world....I *want* them to come for me. Anything's better than this waiting."

_____

_____

_____

29. "Now I think we are friends, this girl and me. On her birthday, it was she who gave a gift—to me. It makes me understand that the best standover man I've ever known is not a man at all..."

_____

_____

_____

30. "...I pitied them, though not as much as I felt for the ones I scooped up from various camps in that time. The Germans in basements were pitiable...but at least they had a chance. That basement was not a washroom. They were not sent there for a shower. For those people, life was still achievable."

_____

_____

_____

D. Essay: Choose one of the following prompts. On a separate sheet of paper, respond in a well-developed essay. Be sure to use specific details from the novel to support your response.

(Compare/Contrast)
a. Compare and contrast the common perception of Death (i.e., The Grim Reaper) with the representation in the novel. Which persona is more conceivable, and why?

(Author's Purpose)
b. Why do you think the author chose to personify Death by making him the narrator of the story?

(Character Analysis)
c. Examine one of the relationships Liesel forges through words. Describe how words contributed to the formation of the relationship, as well as the qualities of the relationship that make it important and valuable to Liesel. How, also, is the relationship valuable to the other person involved?

Answer Key

Activity #1: Dedication—For Elisabeth and Helmut Zusak, with love and admiration; Title—*The Book Thief*; Cover Illustration—finger poised to knock down a row of dominoes; Teasers on the cover—"The Extraordinary *New York Times* #1 Bestseller," "BRILLIANT and hugely ambitious....It's the kind of book that can be LIFE CHANGING"; Friends' recommendations—Answers will vary; Reviewers' recommendations/awards won—"A major achievement."—*People*, Book Sense Book of the Year Award, Michael L. Printz Honor Book, National Jewish Book Award

Activities #2–#3: Answers will vary.

Activity #4: Students will play the Vocabulary Card Game.

Activity #5: Sentences will vary.

Activity #6: Answers will vary. Example: Word—emulate; Definition—to copy the actions of; Synonyms—follow, mimic, imitate; Word used in a sentence—The Hitler Youth organization taught children to *emulate* Adolf Hitler.

Activity #7: Answers will vary.

Activity #8: Associations will vary. Suggestion: Word—hapless; Character—Frau Holtzapfel; Explanation—After losing one son in the war and another to suicide, Frau Holtzapfel was *hapless* and inconsolable.

Activity #9: 1. shrewder 2. cluster 3. tenaciously 4. villains 5. furious 6. reproved 7. watch; Sentences will vary.

Activity #10: Crossword puzzles will vary.

Study Guide
Death and Chocolate–The Kiss (A Childhood Decision Maker): 1. distraction 2. The train is stopped due to a snowstorm. A mother and a child are standing beside the dead body of another child, most likely a son/brother. Two guards are wondering what to do with them. 3. It is the site of a plane crash, and the pilot has died. Years have passed since the first incident. 4. A town has been bombed. 5. a book dropped by one of the grave diggers 6. Playing on the common phrase, "continued like nothing had happened," the book thief is conveying the horrible impact her brother's death has on her. 7. She is frightened and refuses to get out of the car. When she places her hands on the gate, she is hesitant to enter the house. 8. They are brown, as opposed to the Aryan-preferred blue. 9. Communist 10. Mama and Papa 11. plays the accordion 12. She is Lutheran, while the school is predominantly Catholic. She cannot read or write and is put into a lower class. 13. Hitler Youth or BDM 14. to local bars to play his accordion 15. the mayor's wife; She thinks she is crazy and cheap. 16. She spits on it. 17. They must say "*Heil* Hitler." 18. If Rudy wins, Liesel has to kiss him. If Liesel wins, she no longer has to play goalie in soccer.

The Jesse Owens Incident–Dead Letters: 1. He charcoals his face and runs around the track pretending to be Jesse Owens in the 1936 Olympics. 2. one of Alex Steiner's long-time Jewish customers who owned a shoe store destroyed by the Nazis 3. *The Grave Digger's Handbook* 4. Hans teaches Liesel to read. 5. They paint them on the basement wall. 6. Hans' smells— cigarettes and kerosene 7. She is becoming disruptive. 8. She freezes and begins to recite words from *The Grave Digger's Handbook*, an act for which she is beaten. 9. She beats him up. 10. the Germans' love of burning things 11. Papa sold his cigarettes. 12. He can no longer afford to have his laundry done. 13. She thinks they are less likely to fire her if there is a child standing before them. 14. her mother

Hitler's Birthday, 1940–The Attributes of Summer: 1. Hitler's birthday 2. The Jews living there have been deported. It is "awaiting…renovation" and was "ransacked one last time," meaning it has already been mostly destroyed (p. 102). 3. Hans Jr. is an avid Nazi, and his father is not. 4. coward 5. He talks about ridding Germany not only of Jews but of Communists. 6. Ludwig Schmeikl, the boy she beat up at school 7. slaps her across the face 8. It begins to smoke and burn against her skin. 9. a copy of *Mein Kampf* 10. She thinks the mayor's wife saw her take the book from the bonfire. 11. her library 12. food, water, an identification card, a key, a map, and a book 13. The protagonist is a Jew who is presented in a positive light, and the Nazis forbid this. 14. She had a son, Johann, who died in World War I. She maintains her cold and austere existence as a way of mourning. 15. They join a gang of boys who steal apples from local farmers.

The Aryan Shopkeeper–Liesel's Lecture: 1. a piece of hard candy 2. He reads *Mein Kampf*, a book written by his worst enemy. 3. Walter Kugler, his friend from childhood 4. "my struggle"; Max is protected by reading the words of the man who wishes him dead. 5. They will throw water in the road to build up the ice. When Otto rides over it on his bike he will wipe out. Rudy and Liesel will take the basket of food he is carrying. 6. return it to him 7. The farmer chases the kids with an ax. Rudy gets caught on the fence, and Liesel and Arthur have to save him. 8. He marks his steps in sets of 13, for "luck." 9. "Hans Hubermann?" and "Do you still play the accordion?" (p. 173) 10. writing letters for the captain 11. If she ever needs anything, Hans will help her. 12. because he did not join the Nazi Party 13. He repaints Joel Kleinmann's door after the Nazis painted "Jewish filth" on it. 14. Walter Kugler approaches Hans about taking in Max. Hiding a Jew is a huge risk. 15. They fought one another in neighborhood fistfights. 16. a piece of paper with Hans Hubermann's address written on it 17. He sent it to Walter to give to Max with the key to his house taped inside. 18. After one brief explosion, she feeds him her infamous pea soup. 19. He will burn her books if she tells anyone about Max being there. Also, he warns that he, Rosa, and Max would all be taken away by the Nazis.

The Sleeper–The Gamblers (A Seven-Sided Die): 1. "They both arrived in a state of agitation on Himmel Street. They both nightmared" (p. 206). 2. "Thank you;" Racked by guilt for surviving and for putting the Hubermanns in danger, these words seem completely inadequate. 3. guilt and shame 4. Her face is gentler, and she does not yell as much. She is "a good woman for a crisis" (p. 211). 5. They tell her nothing. They keep his presence a secret, since they are uncertain they can trust her. 6. feathers 7. "It's the best book ever.…It saved my life" (p. 217). 8. their nightmares 9. a hug; He is surprised and embarrassed, and he vows to give her something in return. 10. the pages of *Mein Kampf* 11. The quote refers to the illustration on the last page of Max's book, which has a painting of Max and Liesel hanging in the basement. 12. He says mystery bores him. He is more interested in how people arrive at the end than in the end results. 13. "There's a Jew in my basement" (p. 245). 14. the crossword puzzles 15. Liesel's description of the weather 16. being in a boxing ring and fighting Adolf Hitler 17. He thinks it is hypocritical to tell the citizens of Molching that harder times are coming while he is still paying someone to do his laundry. 18. the ghost of her dead brother; Answers will vary, but students should infer that Liesel's brother is acting as her conscience.

Rudy's Youth–The Floating Book (Part II): 1. He tries to defend Tommy Müller, whose bad hearing keeps making him mess up. 2. He does not need the food. He has everything he needs but just wants more. 3. It is a collection of random thoughts, ideas, and sketches. 4. Franz makes him do drills in cow manure. 5. the book she had thrown back at the mayor's wife, *The Whistler* 6. Liesel's shoes 7. a potato 8. When is Hitler's birthday? 9. He pins Rudy down and hacks his hair off with a knife. 10. He is able to join a different division. 11. He throws Liesel's book into the river.

Death's Diary: 1942–Death's Diary: The Parisians: 1. every person—"Find yourself a mirror…" (p. 307). 2. a snowman with snow Liesel brings down in buckets 3. Max fought back and drove Death away. 4. a crushed soccer ball 5. When Liesel sees a particularly good cloud one day, she writes down the description and reads it to him. 6. The title reminds her of the dreams she and Max have. 7. Perhaps the mayor's wife is intentionally leaving the window open for Liesel. 8. what they will do with Max's body if he dies 9. She is back on the train with her dying brother, but her brother turns into Max. 10. to yell at Liesel about a lost hairbrush 11. the toy soldier she had given Max while he was sick 12. empty fuel tanks 13. They are looking for more basements to serve as bomb shelters. 14. She purposely collides with another soccer player so she can get hurt and go home. 15. exhausted, confused, troubled, sad

Champagne and Accordions–The Idiot and the Coat Men: 1. People hire him to paint their blackout blinds. 2. his accordion 3. champagne 4. She would never be able to play like Hans, evoking the same feelings with her music. 5. He is disqualified for two false starts; Answers will vary. 6. It is green, and she does not have a green book yet. 7. a letter to Liesel from Ilsa Hermann 8. He went upstairs and looked outside. 9. She reads to them from *The Whistler*. 10. Two apartment buildings are destroyed, and there is a huge bomb crater in one of the Hitler Youth fields. 11. continue reading from *The Whistler* 12. He offers an old, collapsing Jew a piece of bread. 13. Max leaves because the Nazis will most likely be coming to the house to punish Hans. 14. "You've done enough" (p. 398). 15. He wants to know that Max left for a good reason.

Dominoes and Darkness–The Anarchist's Suit Collection: 1. dominoes 2. They want to put him in a special elite school for the brightest and most athletic children. His parents are fearful because of rumors of cruel experimentation done on children there. 3. They are drafted into the army. 4. She dumps a bucket of cold water on his head. 5. He says he is going to find the *Führer* and kill him. 6. sitting on the edge of her bed with Hans' accordion strapped to her chest 7. Alex mends uniforms and underwear in an army hospital. Hans shores up buildings and collects dead bodies after bombings. 8. They cannot bring themselves to tell her the truth, and they want to prolong her hope just a little longer.

9. reading to Frau Holtzapfel 10. bits of bread for the Jews to pick up and eat 11. Max's sketchbook 12. He sees a mother scold her son, and the young boy begins to cry. 13. a suit from his father's shop

The Next Temptation–Homecoming: 1. a plate of cookies 2. swastikas 3. because he beat him in cards 4. Three of his fingers were blown off in a battle at Stalingrad. 5. His legs were blown off, and he received a stomach wound in Stalingrad. He died three days later in a Russian hospital. 6. the empty plate from the cookies 7. She sits with the accordion strapped to her, praying for Hans' and Alex's safe return. 8. In an attempt to get back at Hans, Zucker took Hans' seat in the truck. When the truck flipped over, Zucker broke his neck because of where he was sitting. 9. He broke his leg in the truck accident. 10. He says if a kid walks in on him he will give it to him to calm him down. 11. His desire to steal was driven by the desire to take something back from the Nazis, but he realizes he is not really a thief and cannot go through with it. 12. She refuses to move from her kitchen. 13. Death 14. the teddy bear that he was going to use during his thefts 15. Hans

The End of the World (Part I)–The Handover Man: 1. She was in her basement writing the story of her life. 2. soft 3. He suffers guilt for living when his brother died and for leaving his mother during the bombing raid. 4. Snow is falling. 5. She quotes *The Word Shaker*: "'There was once a strange, small man'.…But there was a word shaker, too" (p. 512). 6. They are both whipped. 7. She realizes she loves Rudy. 8. She is angry over all the ugliness she has had to witness. She does not want to be comforted by the words in a book when words are what gave Hitler his power. 9. She brings Liesel a blank book in which she can write her life story. 10. She tries to wake him and gives him the kiss he so longed for. 11. She sees his body rise up and play the accordion for her one last time. 12. Liesel's book, *The Book Thief* 13. as an old woman in Sydney, Australia 14. to live with the Hermanns 15. Max 16. *The Book Thief* 17. "I am haunted by humans"; Answers will vary (p. 550).

Note: Responses to Activities #11–#21 will vary. Suggested answers have been given where applicable.

Activity #11: Main Characters—Death (narrator), Liesel Meminger, Hans Hubermann, Rosa Hubermann, Max Vandenburg, Rudy Steiner, Ilsa Hermann; Setting—Molching, Germany just prior to and during World War II; Main Conflict—Liesel tries to adjust to life with her foster family in World War II Germany, stealing books and befriending a runaway Jew; Summary of Major Story Events—Liesel is left in Molching by her mother after the death of Liesel's brother, Werner. Liesel is haunted by bad dreams; Hans Hubermann tenderly cares for her, keeping her company at night and teaching her to read. Liesel befriends Rudy, a spirited young boy. Liesel, driven by her newfound love of reading and a desire to take things back from Hitler, begins stealing books. Max Vandenburg, the son of one of Hans' war friends, arrives at the house to hide from the Nazis. Max falls terribly ill, and the family worriedly awaits his fate. Liesel and Rudy begin stealing books from Ilsa Hermann's library. Alex Steiner and Hans are drafted into the army. Liesel spots Max in a group of Jewish prisoners marching to Dachau concentration camp. Ilsa Hermann gives Liesel a blank book in which to write her story. While writing in the basement, Liesel survives a bombing that kills everyone else on Himmel Street; Climax—the bombing of Himmel Street; Resolution of Conflict—Liesel goes to live with the Hermanns. Alex Steiner returns from the war when he learns his wife and children are dead. Max, having survived the concentration camp, returns to Molching to find Liesel after the war.

Activity #12: Victims—Death (figuratively), Ilsa Hermann, Max, Frau Holtzapfel, ultimately Michael and Robert Holtzapfel, Rudy, Hans, Rosa; Victimizers: Death (literally), Adolf Hitler, Franz Deutscher, Viktor Chemmel; Fighters: Max, Liesel, Rudy, Alex Steiner (for refusing to give up Rudy); Peace-lovers: Hans, Rudy, Max; Conformists: Frau Diller, Frau Holtzapfel, Alex Steiner; Self-directors: Rosa, Rudy

Activity #13: Liesel—friendship, words, beauty; Hans—keeping promises, compassion, music; Rosa—personal strength, perseverance, family; Rudy—life, love, winning; Max—survival, friendship, fighting; Ilsa Hermann—the memory of her dead son, Liesel, books

Activity #14: Example for Liesel—1. Liesel steals her first book at her brother's gravesite. 2. Liesel learns to accept the Hubermanns' love. 3. Liesel befriends and encourages Max. 4. Liesel is able to apologize to Ilsa Hermann and therefore end her bad dreams. 5. Liesel writes her story, even though all of her loved ones are dead and she hasn't any hope left.

Activity #15: Example for Liesel and Hans—Liesel: feels abandoned, struggling to make sense of the world, lover of words, true friend; Hans: feels guilty for surviving World War I, gentle, lover of music, fair; Liesel to Hans: adores him, learns from him; Hans to Liesel: nurtures and tends to her, teaches her to read

Activity #16: Answers will vary.

Activity #17: Example for Max—1. Eric Vandenburg volunteers Hans in World War I, saving him from death in battle. 2. Hans visits Eric's widow and offers to help if they ever need anything. 3. Max, in need of a place to hide from the Nazis, seeks help from Hans. 4. The Hubermanns hide Max in their basement. 5. Max decides to leave the Hubermanns' because Nazis may come to the house after Hans gives bread to a Jew. 6. Max is caught and sent to Dachau concentration camp, but he survives.

Activity #18: person vs. person—Max's fantasies involve a boxing match with Adolf Hitler. Although only in his mind, this fight keeps him going. Resolution—Max defeats Hitler (figuratively) by surviving the concentration camp; person vs. nature—All characters are in conflict with Death. Resolution—Some die early, some live long lives, but Death inevitably wins; person vs. society—Hans is ridiculed for giving bread to a Jew. Resolution: Hans is sent to clean up after air raids; person vs. self—Michael Holtzapfel feels extreme guilt and shame for surviving while his brother died in the war. Resolution—Michael commits suicide.

Activity #19: Possible themes—the power of words, love, friendship, survival, grief, courage, death, forgiveness, the complexities of the human condition

Activity #20: Liesel—stole books and connected with Max through reading; Hans—helped him bond with Liesel as he taught her to read; Max—kept him in touch with the outside world and connected him to Liesel; Frau Holtzapfel—Liesel's reading kept her calm during the air raids; Ilsa Hermann—owned her own library and connected with Liesel through the stolen books; Rudy—connected him to Liesel as he helped her steal books; citizens of Molching—believed in Nazi ideals due to Hitler's powerful speeches

Activity #21: Answers will vary.

Quiz #1: A. 1. f 2. h 3. a 4. j 5. b 6. e 7. c 8. g 9. k 10. d 11. i **B.** 12. Germany during World War II 13. They are her foster parents since her mother is being taken away. 14. grave digging 15. Rosa does washing for her neighbors, and Hans paints and plays the accordion. 16. Ludwig Schmeikl makes fun of her illiteracy.

Quiz #2: A. 1. fist fighting 2. play the accordion 3. the priests 4. write letters for the captain 5. key/book/map 6. "my struggle" 7. painting his door **B.** 8. T 9. F 10. F 11. T 12. T 13. F 14. T **C.** 15. metonymy 16. simile 17. personification 18. metaphor

Quiz #3: A. 1. c 2. f 3. c 4. g 5. a 6. d 7. g 8. d 9. e 10. h 11. g 12. g 13. f 14. d 15. h 16. b (p. 211) 17. i 18. g 19. c 20. i **B.** Answers will vary. Refer to the scoring rubric on page 48 of this guide.

Quiz #4: A. 1. b (p. 332) 2. e (p. 309) 3. c (p. 364) 4. h (p. 369) 5. g (p. 378) 6. a (p. 387) 7. d (p. 400) 8. f (p. 316) **B.** 9. T 10. F 11. F 12. T 13. F 14. F 15. T

Quiz #5: 1. because he would not send Rudy to an elite Nazi school 2. Max; as a gift to Liesel 3. sitting and praying with Hans' accordion strapped on her chest 4. bread; He and Liesel are chased by Nazi guards. 5. shoring up buildings and collecting dead bodies after bombings 6. to his father's shop; a suit 7. a broken leg 8. His brother, Robert, is dead. 9. a teddy bear 10. inside a mattress

Quiz #6: A. Title—*The Book Thief*; Author—Markus Zusak; Setting—Molching, Germany just prior to and during World War II; Main Characters—Liesel, Hans, Rosa, Rudy, Max, Alex Steiner, Ilsa Hermann; Conflict—Liesel is trying to adjust to life with her foster family during the war; Themes—survival, guilt, friendship, love, grief, death, the human condition; Author's Style/Tone—candid and sad **B.** Answers will vary, but students should note the following: Liesel lives through the war and raises a family in Australia; Rudy is killed in the bombing of Himmel Street; Alex Steiner returns from the war when his family is killed and reopens his shop; Ilsa takes in Liesel after the Hubermanns are killed; Hans and Rosa are killed in the bombing of Himmel Street; Max survives Dachau concentration camp and reunites with Liesel at Alex Steiner's shop after the war. Refer to the scoring rubric on page 48 of this guide.

Novel Test: A. 1. l 2. b (p. 440) 3. a 4. d (p. 211) 5. h 6. k 7. r 8. f 9. i 10. q 11. p 12. e 13. m 14. c 15. n 16. s 17. o 18. j 19. g 20. t **B.** 21. personification 22. simile 23. metonymy 24. metaphor **C.** 25. Liesel (p. 522); the power of words—In a note to Ilsa Hermann, Liesel explains why she destroyed a book. This comes at a time of great distress for Liesel because she has just seen Max march by. Liesel is realizing how words can be used both for good and evil and is thus conflicted between her love for words and her fear of them. 26. Death (p. 491); the complexities of the human condition—Throughout the novel, Death is mystified by how humans can be so admirable at one moment and so unworthy the next. Hitler serves as the epitome of evil, but other characters in the novel also illustrate how poorly humans can treat each other, e.g., townspeople's attitudes as the Jews are marched through town. Conversely, the reader is witness to several heroic acts, e.g., the Hubermanns protecting Max, Hans and Rudy both offering bread to Jewish prisoners, Rosa's and Hans' kindness to Liesel. 27. Michael Holtzapfel (p. 504); guilt and grief—In his suicide note to his mother, Michael expresses his inability to continue living with guilt, shame, and grief over his brother's death. He attempts to explain to his mother that although he does not wish to leave her, his need to end his own suffering and "meet" his brother is far greater. 28. Hans (p. 402); grief—Hans knows that giving the bread to the starving Jew was the right thing to do, but he is consumed with thoughts of the danger in which he has put his family and Max. He grieves not only for the Jews that need help, but for his incapacity to provide that help without hurting his own family. He wants to be punished by the Nazis; at least then he would no longer fear retribution for his loved ones. 29. Max (p. 235); friendship—These are the last lines of Max's book for Liesel, *The Standover Man*. The book is a symbol of Max and Liesel's deep friendship, a friendship that transcends all the ugliness brought on by Hitler. Max finds it ironic that after relying on men for his own survival for so long, the person who most makes him want to live is a young girl. 30. Death (p. 376); death—Death is remarking at the audacity of Germans to hide and fear for their lives during air raids. Some of these were the same people who believed that Jews deserved to die, in the most inhumane and undignified manners. While the Germans may have been facing their own deaths, if they *did* survive they would at least be allowed to go back to their daily lives without fear. **D.** Essays will vary. Refer to the scoring rubric on page 48 of this guide.

Linking Novel Units® Student Packets to National and State Reading Assessments

During the past several years, an increasing number of students have faced some form of state-mandated competency testing in reading. Many states now administer state-developed assessments to measure the skills and knowledge emphasized in their particular reading curriculum. This Novel Units® guide includes open-ended comprehension questions that correlate with state-mandated reading assessments. The rubric below provides important information for evaluating responses to open-ended comprehension questions. Teachers may also use scoring rubrics provided for their own state's competency test.

Scoring Rubric for Open-Ended Items

3-Exemplary	Thorough, complete ideas/information Clear organization throughout Logical reasoning/conclusions Thorough understanding of reading task Accurate, complete response
2-Sufficient	Many relevant ideas/pieces of information Clear organization throughout most of response Minor problems in logical reasoning/conclusions General understanding of reading task Generally accurate and complete response
1-Partially Sufficient	Minimally relevant ideas/information Obvious gaps in organization Obvious problems in logical reasoning/conclusions Minimal understanding of reading task Inaccuracies/incomplete response
0-Insufficient	Irrelevant ideas/information No coherent organization Major problems in logical reasoning/conclusions Little or no understanding of reading task Generally inaccurate/incomplete response